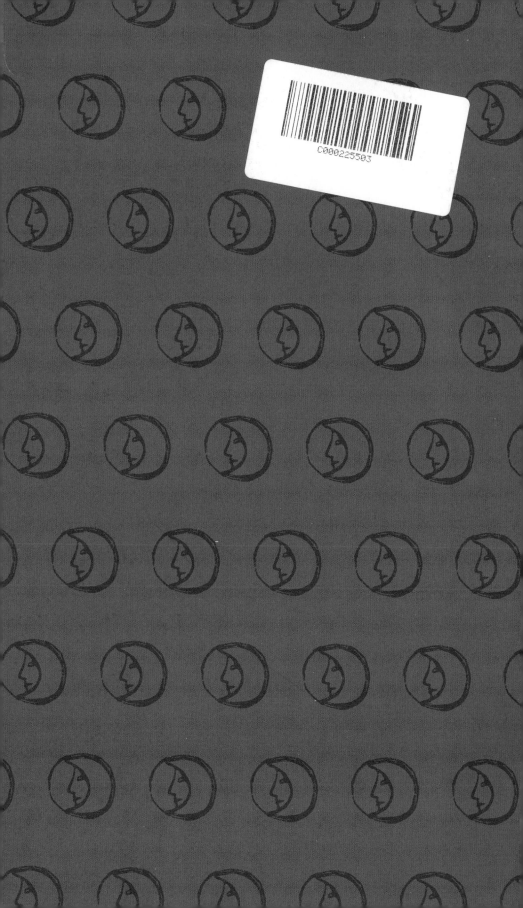

JOURNEYS

First published in the U.K. in 2004
by HarperCollins*Publishers*

Copyright © Paulo Coelho and Mosaikk AS, 2004
www.paulocoelho.com

Published in agreement with
Sant Jordi Asociados Agencia Literaria, S.L., Barcelona, Spain
www.santjordi-asociados.com

Produced by Mosaikk AS, Oslo, Norway
Text selection and editing: Marcia Botelho
English translation copyright © Margaret Jull Costa, 2004
Illustrations: Anne Kristin Hagesæther
Photographs © Xavier González
Graphic designer: Lene Stangebye Geving
Production manager: Rolf Malmberg
Printed and bound at Korotan Ljubljana Ltd., 2004

ISBN 0-00-719339-4

PAULO COELHO

JOURNEYS

A companion & journal

HarperCollins*Publishers*

Date

Time

The fear of suffering is worse than suffering itself.

THE ALCHEMIST

Date

_____

Time

_____

Sometimes happiness is a blessing,
but generally it is a conquest.

BY THE RIVER PIEDRA I SAT DOWN AND WEPT

Date

_____

Time

_____

It is precisely the possibility of realizing a dream
that makes life interesting.
THE ALCHEMIST

Date

Time

Don't try to be brave when it is enough to be intelligent.

THE PILGRIMAGE

Date

_____

Time

_____

No one can make a choice without feeling fear.
BRIDA

Date

_____

Time

_____

Faith is difficult to conquer and requires
daily battles if it is to be maintained.

THE VALKYRIES

Date

_____

Time

_____

The closer you get to your dream,
the more your personal legend
becomes your real reason for living.
THE ALCHEMIST

Date

Time

The strongest love
is the love that can demonstrate its fragility.
ELEVEN MINUTES

Date

Time

There is no point in understanding
the entire Universe if you are all alone.
BRIDA

Date

_____

Time

_____

The simplest things are the most extraordinary,
and only the wise can see them.
THE ALCHEMIST

Date

_____

Time

_____

Date

Time

The Lord listens to the prayers of those who ask
to be able to forget hatred,
but is deaf to those who want to flee love.

THE FIFTH MOUNTAIN

Date

_____

Time

_____

Dreams must be talked about
before they can begin to be realized.
THE PILGRIMAGE

Date

———————————

Time

———————————

No man is an island.
To fight the Good Fight we need help.
THE PILGRIMAGE

Date

_____

Time

_____

The Universe always conspires to help dreamers.

BY THE RIVER PIEDRA I SAT DOWN AND WEPT

Do not offer up to God only the pain of your penitence,
offer Him your joys as well.

THE PILGRIMAGE

Date

_____

Time

_____

We lose many things
simply out of fear of losing them.
BRIDA

Date

_____

Time

_____

Pain is in our daily lives, in our hidden suffering,
in the sacrifices we make
and we blame love for the destruction of our dreams.
ELEVEN MINUTES

Date

_____

Time

_____

All suffering goes just as it came.
So it is with the glories and the tragedies
of the world.

THE FIFTH MOUNTAIN

The world lies in the hands of those who have the courage
to dream and take the risk of living out their dreams
– each according to his or her own talent.

THE VALKYRIES

Date

———————————————

Time

———————————————

God always offers us a second chance in life.
BY THE RIVER PIEDRA I SAT DOWN AND WEPT

Date

_____

Time

_____

Never give up on your dreams – follow the signs.
THE ALCHEMIST

Date

——————————————

Time

——————————————

Life moves very fast.
It rushes us from heaven to hell in a matter of seconds.
ELEVEN MINUTES

Date

_____

Time

_____

Sorrows do not last for ever when we are journeying
towards the thing we have always wanted.
THE FIFTH MOUNTAIN

Date

_____

Time

_____

Suffering, if confronted without fear,
is the great passport to freedom.

ELEVEN MINUTES

Date

Time

Only the happy can spread happiness.

BY THE RIVER PIEDRA I SAT DOWN AND WEPT

Date

_____

Time

_____

The path teaches us the best way to arrive
and enriches us while we are travelling along it.

THE PILGRIMAGE

Date

Time

*We're allowed to make many mistakes in our lives,
but not the mistake that will destroy us.*
VERONIKA DECIDES TO DIE

Date

_____

Time

_____

You do not drown simply by plunging into water,
you only drown if you stay beneath the surface.

MANUAL OF THE WARRIOR OF LIGHT

Date

_____

Time

_____

Everyone has the right to doubt his task
and to abandon it now and then;
the only thing he cannot do is to forget it.
THE FIFTH MOUNTAIN

God is always the same,
even though He may have a thousand names;
but you need to choose a name to call Him by.

BY THE RIVER PIEDRA I SAT DOWN AND WEPT

Date

_____

Time

_____

Making mistakes is a way of taking action.
ELEVEN MINUTES

Date

_____

Time

_____

There is always a right moment to stop something.

ELEVEN MINUTES

Date

Time

To each of man's ages the Lord gives its own anxieties.

THE FIFTH MOUNTAIN

Date

Time

How does light enter a person?
Through the open door of love.
ELEVEN MINUTES

Date

Time

Even a difficult, winding path can lead to your goal
if you do not deviate from that path in any way.

MAKTUB

Date

Time

When we put off the harvest, the fruit rots,
but when we put off our problems, they keep on growing.

THE FIFTH MOUNTAIN

Date

_____

Time

_____

Sometimes we have only ten minutes
to be with the love of our life and
thousands of hours to spend thinking about them.

ELEVEN MINUTES

Date

Time

The first indication that we are killing our dreams is lack of time.

THE PILGRIMAGE

Courage. By beginning the journey with that word
and continuing with faith in God,
you will arrive wherever you need to arrive.

MANUAL OF THE WARRIOR OF LIGHT

Date

Time

Be like the fountain that overflows,
not like the cistern that merely contains.
VERONIKA DECIDES TO DIE

A search always starts with Beginner's Luck
and ends with the Test of the Conqueror.

THE ALCHEMIST

Date

_____

Time

_____

Date

_____

Time

_____

Life always waits for some crisis to occur
before revealing itself at its most brilliant.

ELEVEN MINUTES

Date

Time

When we set out in search of the treasure,
we realize that the path itself is the treasure.
THE ALCHEMIST

Date

Time

The Lord only demands of us
what is within our capabilities.

THE FIFTH MOUNTAIN

Date

_____

Time

_____

God judges a tree by its fruits and not by its roots.

MANUAL OF THE WARRIOR OF LIGHT

Date

_____

Time

_____

Love is not to be found in someone else, but in ourselves;
we simply awaken it.
But in order to do that, we need the other person.

ELEVEN MINUTES

Date

_____

Time

_____

Love cannot exist in peace,
it will always come accompanied by agonies, ecstasies,
intense joys and profound sadnesses.

THE VALKYRIES

The path of magic - and, generally speaking, the path of
life itself - is and always will be the path of mystery.

BRIDA

Date

_____

Time

_____

*Sometimes we insist on seeing the mote in the eye and
forget about the mountains, fields and olive groves.*
BY THE RIVER PIEDRA I SAT DOWN AND WEPT

Date

Time

Every day, God gives us, as well as the sun,
a moment when it is possible to change anything
that is causing us unhappiness.

BY THE RIVER PIEDRA I SAT DOWN AND WEPT

Many people get caught up in the detail
and forget what they are looking for.

THE PILGRIMAGE

Date

Time

We must make the most of the times
when luck is on our side and do everything to help it,
just as it is helping us.

THE ALCHEMIST

Set off along your path with courage
and do not fear the criticism of others.
Above all, do not allow yourself
to be paralyzed by self-criticism.

MAKTUB

Date

Time

The second indication of the death of our dreams
is certainty.

THE PILGRIMAGE

A warrior accepts defeat. He does not treat it as a matter
of indifference nor does he try to make a victory out of it.

MANUAL OF THE WARRIOR OF LIGHT

Date

_____

Time

_____

Only those who find life find treasure.

THE ALCHEMIST

Date

_____

Time

_____

Every human being has inside them something more
important than him or herself – his or her gift.

B R I D A

Date

Time

Accumulating love brings luck,
accumulating hatred brings calamity.

MANUAL OF THE WARRIOR OF LIGHT

Date

_____

Time

_____

The third indication that our dreams are dead is peace.
Life becomes one long Sunday afternoon
if we do not ask great things of ourselves
and do not demand more of ourselves than we can give.
We are, in short, refusing to fight for our dreams.

THE PILGRIMAGE

Date

Time

The warrior of light makes use of solitude,
but is not used by it.

MANUAL OF THE WARRIOR OF LIGHT

If the strings of an instrument are always taut,
they go out of tune.

MANUAL OF THE WARRIOR OF LIGHT

Date

Time

When God wants to make someone mad,
He satisfies all their desires.

THE VALKYRIES

It is necessary to run risks and not be afraid of defeat.

BRIDA

Date

_____

Time

_____

Love is risky, but then it always has been.
People have been looking for and finding each other
for thousands of years.

BRIDA

Date

_____

Time

_____

There are moments when people are incapable
of understanding happiness.
VERONIKA DECIDES TO DIE

Date

Time

When we least expect it, life sets us a challenge
to test our courage and willingness to change.

THE DEVIL AND MISS PRYM

Date

Time

When we have great treasures before us,
we cannot see them.

THE ALCHEMIST

Date
_____

Time
_____

We are all masters of our own destinies.
BRIDA

Date

_____

Time

_____

There are three things that a child can teach an adult:
to be happy for no reason; always to be busy doing
something; and to know how to demand
- with all one's might - what one wants.

THE FIFTH MOUNTAIN

Date

Time

Choosing one path means abandoning others
– if you try to follow every possible path
you will end up following none.

BRIDA

Date

Time

Everyone has their own way of learning.
THE ALCHEMIST

It hurt when I lost each of the men I fell in love with.
Now, though, I am convinced that no one loses anyone,
because no one owns anyone. That is the true experience
of freedom: having the most important thing in the
world without owning it.

ELEVEN MINUTES

Date

Time

If you go around promising what you do not yet have,
you will lose the will to achieve it.

THE ALCHEMIST

In order for things to improve,
you must know what you want.

BRIDA

Date

Time

The great victory, which appears so simple today,
was the result of a series of small victories
that went unnoticed.

MANUAL OF THE WARRIOR OF LIGHT

Date

Time

*When we love, it is not necessary to understand
what is happening outside, because everything begins
to happen inside us instead.*
THE ALCHEMIST

Date

_____

Time

_____

Wagers and pacts are made with angels – or with devils.
THE VALKYRIES

Date

———————————————

Time

———————————————

Each stretch of road travelled enriches the pilgrim
and brings him a little closer to realizing his dreams.

THE ALCHEMIST

Date

_____

Time

_____

No one can avoid defeat.
That is why it is better to lose a few battles in the fight
for your dreams than to be defeated
without even knowing why you are fighting.

BY THE RIVER PIEDRA I SAT DOWN AND WEPT

Date

Time

When you look directly into someone's eyes,
they become incapable of lying or concealing anything.

BY THE RIVER PIEDRA I SAT DOWN AND WEPT

Date
_____

Time
_____

There are moments when troubles enter our lives
and we can do nothing to avoid them.
But they are there for a reason.
Only when we have overcome them
will we understand why.

THE FIFTH MOUNTAIN

Date

Time

A man has to choose.
Therein lies his strength: in the power of his decisions.
THE FIFTH MOUNTAIN

Date

_____

Time

_____

Certain people, in their eagerness to construct
a world which no external threat can penetrate,
build high defences against the outside world and leave
their inner world stripped bare.

VERONIKA DECIDES TO DIE

Date

Time

Anyone who loves
in the expectation of being loved in return
is wasting their time.

THE DEVIL AND MISS PRYM

Never let doubt paralyze your actions.
Always make the decisions you need to make,
even if you are not sure you are making the right decisions.

BRIDA

Date

_____

Time

_____

The glory of the world is transitory,
and we should not measure our lives by it,
but by the choice we make to follow our personal legend,
believe in our utopias and fight for our dreams.

ACCEPTANCE SPEECH DELIVERED TO
THE BRAZILIAN ACADEMY OF LETTERS

Free yourself from all those wretched ideas,
from that mania for explaining everything
and only doing what others will approve of.

BY THE RIVER PIEDRA I SAT DOWN AND WEPT

Date

_____

Time

_____

*It is always easier to hear an insult and not respond
than to have the courage to engage in combat
with someone stronger than yourself.*

THE DEVIL AND MISS PRYM

God created the desert so that man could smile
when he saw the palm tree.
THE ALCHEMIST

Date

_____

Time

_____

It is not a sin to be happy.

THE PILGRIMAGE

Date

Time

A blessing rejected becomes a curse.

THE ALCHEMIST

Waiting hurts. Forgetting hurts.
But not knowing which decision to take
is the worst of sufferings.

BY THE RIVER PIEDRA I SAT DOWN AND WEPT

Date

Time

People can be divided into those who build and those who
plant. Those who build finish their task and, one day,
are overcome by boredom.
Those who plant are subject to rain and storm,
but the garden will never stop growing.

BRIDA

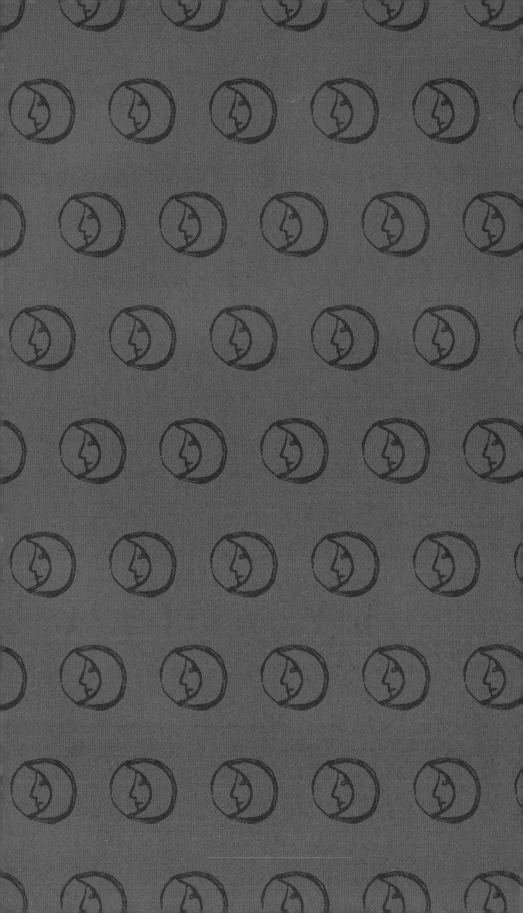